Dell
and His Dot

adapted from the story written by
Beverly Cory

illustrations by
James Balkovek

Good Morning Teacher! Publishing Company
Maker of Brain Tools for the Young Mind™
San Mateo, California

This is Dell.

He has a dot.

The dot can sit on Dell.

Dell can sit on the dot.

"My dot can hop," says Dell.
"It can hop on my bed.
It can hop on my pack."

"I can hop up the path
 and go fast, fast, fast!" says the dot.

Dell and his dot have a lot of fun.
The dot hides in a pit.
Dell must hunt for his dot.

Dell jumps in the pit, and now he has his dot.

"Oh no!
A big bug is on the dot!" says Dell.
He falls back with a yell.

The bug sits on top of the dot.
The dot hops and hops.
The bug does not like to hop,
but it does like to fly.

Next, the dot hides in a nest.
But a duck sits on the nest,
and the dot must go.

The dot hops to the pond.
Does Dell see the dot?
Yes, he does.
Can Dell get the dot?
No, he gets wet!

The dot hides in a sack.
Does Dell get his dot at last?
"I have my dot back!
The dot is in my sack," says Dell.

This is Matt.

He sees the sack hop.

"How can a sack hop like that?"
asks Matt.

"My dot is in the sack," Dell tells Matt.

14

"I want to see the dot jump," says Matt.
"Jump!" Matt tells the dot.
    The dot jumps,
    but it hits Matt.

Now Matt is mad.
"I will stomp on that dot!" Matt yells.
But the dot is too fast,
and Matt hits a rock.

Then, Matt trips, and he falls with *a bump!*

"That dot is a big pest.
   Get rid of it!" Matt says to Dell.
"I will take my dot
   and go to the park," says Dell.

Dell meets Big Dan at the park.
"Is that a ball in the sack?" asks Big Dan.
"This is not a ball.
It is my dot," Dell tells Big Dan.

"My dot can hop.
It can jump up
to the tip-top of this tree," says Dell.

"If I hang up the dot,
I can box," says Big Dan.
Big Dan hits the dot.
The dot swings back,
and it hits Big Dan.
"This dot is a pest!" yells Big Dan.

Big Dan grabs the dot in his hands.
He and Dell tug and tug,
and the dot rips.

Dell is sad,
but he can mend his dot.
"Matt and Big Dan think
my dot is a pest," Dell says.
"Who will like my dot?" he asks.

"Jan will like my dot!" says Dell.
"I will send it to her."
Dell puts the dot in a box.

This is Jan.
Jan has the box that Dell sent.
"Well, well, well. What is this?
Is this a hat?" asks Jan.
"No, it must not be a hat,"
she says.

"If this is not a hat,
it must be a mat," says Jan.
But Jan can see that the dot
is not a mat.

"I can put it on a rack,
  or I can hang it with a tack," Jan says.

30

Jan asks, "Is it a big mint?"
Does Jan lick the dot?
No, she bites it!
"Mmmm! Not bad!" Jan says.

Jan puts the dot on a dish,
and then she finds a pan.
Jan drops the dot in the pan.

"Jan thinks she can fry me
   in a pan," says the dot.
"That pan will get hot, hot, hot!"
   With a big hop,
   the dot jumps out of the pan.

"Stop the dot!" yells Jan.
"I must run fast
  to get that pest.
The dot can hop,
  and it will not stop."

Dell is sad.

"I miss my dot!" thinks Dell.

Then, the dot hops past Dell.

"That must be my dot!" yells Dell.

"I can ride fast.
I will get my dot," says Dell.
Dell can ride and glide,
but he can not get
his dot.

Dell yells to Matt,
"Help me stop my dot!"

Matt rolls past Dell.
Matt can skate fast.
Can he get the dot?
No, Matt is fast,
but not that fast.

The dot sings:

A dot is fun.
A dot is the best.
A dot can hop.
A dot is NOT a pest!

"I can hop on a hill.
I can hop on a stump.

I can hop on a log
with a bump, bump, bump!"
says the dot.

Is that Big Dan on a bike?
Yes, it is.
Big Dan can ride fast on his bike.
He can ride as fast as the dot.

The dot must hop fast!
The dot hops up, up, up—
to the top of a big hill.

At the top, the dot has to stop.
Big Dan grabs the dot at last!

"This is the dot that hit me.
I will get rid of this pest!" says Big Dan.
Big Dan sends the dot up, up, up—
to the sky.
Can the dot hop in the sky?
No, no, no.

But the dot can fly!
"This is fun!" yells the dot.
It can fly past Dell, Jan, and Matt.

The dot can fly past a big bird!
It can fly by the hot sun!

At last, the dot starts to fall.
"Will I get wet?
Or will I land in the soft sand?"
asks the dot.

The dot does not get wet.
It does not land in the soft sand.
The dot hits the deck of a ship.

On the ship,
a mop scrubs the deck.
The dot must get up.
"Oh no! The mop! The mop!" yells the dot.

Does the mop scrub the dot?
No, the mop hits the dot,
and the dot falls off the ship.
Then, the dot sinks fast.

**Fat fish and thin fish nip at the dot.
At last, a big, green fish eats the dot.
GULP!**

**Dell, Jan, Matt, and Big Dan
fish on a raft.
Dell is sad. "I miss my dot.
I wish I had it back," says Dell.**

Dell has a big, green fish on his rod!
"We can fry that fish,"
Big Dan tells him.

**Jan and Big Dan pick up
the big, green fish.
This is the fish that ate the dot.
"My dot is back!" yells Dell.**

"My dot is wet, wet, wet!" says Dell.
The dot can not sit up.
Dell can tell that his dot is sick.

Matt has a pump.
"Let me try to pump up the dot,"
Matt says to Dell.

58

The pump does the job!
Now the dot can sit up!
Then Dell yells, "Stop, Matt!
The dot must not get that big!"

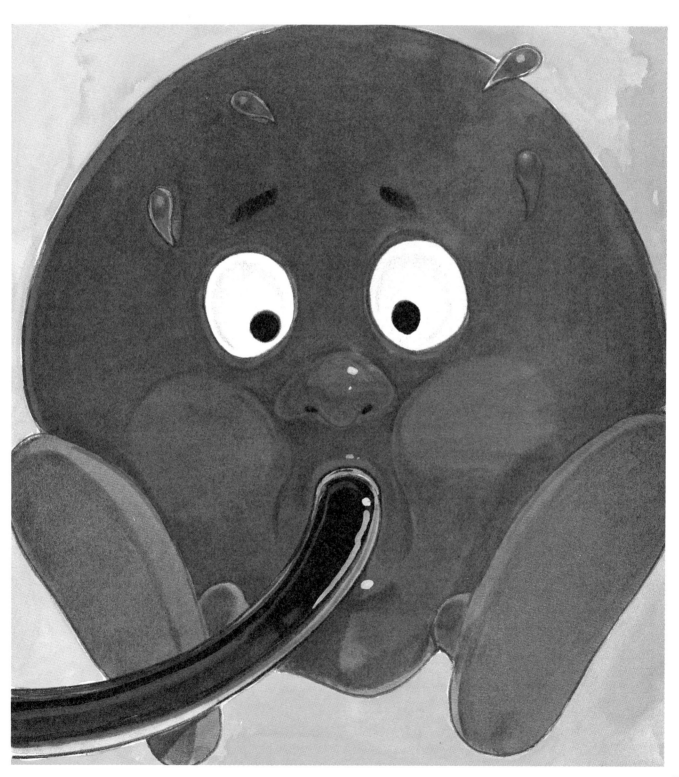

Now, a lot of dots
drop from the sky.

Matt has a dot with red fuzz.
Big Dan has a big dot.
Jan has a dot with a hat.
They like the new dots.

And Dell?
He has a dot—
a dot that can hop.

Dell is not sad.
In fact, Dell is glad.
"A dot is not a pest.
A dot is THE BEST!" says Dell.